I'M SCHEDULING MEETINGS TO FILL THE VOID IN MY LIFE

2000 DESK CALENDAR

DILBERT™

BY SCOTT ADAMS

D1097053

Andrews McMeel
Publishing

an Andrews McMeel Universal company
Kansas City

www.andrewsmcmeel.com

ISBN: 0-8362-9905-1

E-Mail: SCOTTADAMS@AOL.COM
www.dilbert.com

Are you interested in receiving the official publication of
DOGBERT'S NEW RULING CLASS (the DNRC)?

It's FREE! Subscribe automatically via e-mail:

Address: LISTSERV@listserv.unitedmedia.com
Subject: Newsletter
Message: SUBSCRIBE Dilbert_News YourFirstName YourLastName
(Fill in your first and last name only)

Or send your name and address to:
THE DILBERT NEWSLETTER
c/o United Media
200 Madison Avenue
New York, NY 10016

2000

JANUARY

S	M	T	W	T	F	S
						1
2	3	4	5	6	7	8
9	10	11	12	13	14	15
16	17	18	19	20	21	22
23	24	25	26	27	28	29
30	31					

FEBRUARY

S	M	T	W	T	F	S
		1	2	3	4	5
6	7	8	9	10	11	12
13	14	15	16	17	18	19
20	21	22	23	24	25	26
27	28	29				

MARCH

S	M	T	W	T	F	S
			1	2	3	4
5	6	7	8	9	10	11
12	13	14	15	16	17	18
19	20	21	22	23	24	25
26	27	28	29	30	31	

APRIL

S	M	T	W	T	F	S
						1
2	3	4	5	6	7	8
9	10	11	12	13	14	15
16	17	18	19	20	21	22
23	24	25	26	27	28	29
30						

MAY

S	M	T	W	T	F	S
	1	2	3	4	5	6
7	8	9	10	11	12	13
14	15	16	17	18	19	20
21	22	23	24	25	26	27
28	29	30	31			

JUNE

S	M	T	W	T	F	S
				1	2	3
4	5	6	7	8	9	10
11	12	13	14	15	16	17
18	19	20	21	22	23	24
25	26	27	28	29	30	

JULY

S	M	T	W	T	F	S
						1
2	3	4	5	6	7	8
9	10	11	12	13	14	15
16	17	18	19	20	21	22
23	24	25	26	27	28	29
30	31					

AUGUST

S	M	T	W	T	F	S
		1	2	3	4	5
6	7	8	9	10	11	12
13	14	15	16	17	18	19
20	21	22	23	24	25	26
27	28	29	30	31		

SEPTEMBER

S	M	T	W	T	F	S
					1	2
3	4	5	6	7	8	9
10	11	12	13	14	15	16
17	18	19	20	21	22	23
24	25	26	27	28	29	30

OCTOBER

S	M	T	W	T	F	S
1	2	3	4	5	6	7
8	9	10	11	12	13	14
15	16	17	18	19	20	21
22	23	24	25	26	27	28
29	30	31				

NOVEMBER

S	M	T	W	T	F	S
			1	2	3	4
5	6	7	8	9	10	11
12	13	14	15	16	17	18
19	20	21	22	23	24	25
26	27	28	29	30		

DECEMBER

S	M	T	W	T	F	S
					1	2
3	4	5	6	7	8	9
10	11	12	13	14	15	16
17	18	19	20	21	22	23
24	25	26	27	28	29	30
31						

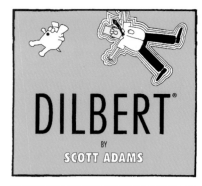

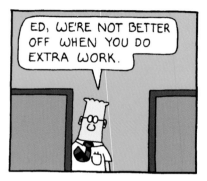

NOTES

NOTES

DEC '99–JAN 2000

DECEMBER 1999

S	M	T	W	T	F	S
			1	2	3	4
5	6	7	8	9	10	11
12	13	14	15	16	17	18
19	20	21	22	23	24	25
26	27	28	29	30	31	

JANUARY 2000

S	M	T	W	T	F	S
						1
2	3	4	5	6	7	8
9	10	11	12	13	14	15
16	17	18	19	20	21	22
23	24	25	26	27	28	29
30	31					

27 MONDAY

28 TUESDAY

29 WEDNESDAY

30 THURSDAY

31 FRIDAY

1 SATURDAY — New Year's Day • Kwanzaa ends

2 SUNDAY

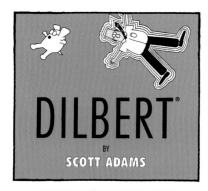

DILBERT

BY **SCOTT ADAMS**

WHY DO I HAVE A FEELING OF IMPENDING DOOM?

GOOD NEWS!

UH-OH.

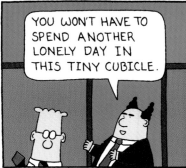

YOU WON'T HAVE TO SPEND ANOTHER LONELY DAY IN THIS TINY CUBICLE.

I'M GETTING AN OFFICE?

BETTER! YOU'RE GETTING A ROOMMATE!

WHY??? WE'VE GOT PLENTY OF EMPTY CUBICLES! OUR COMPANY OWNS THE WHOLE BUILDING!

THE FINANCE DEPARTMENT CHARGES MY BUDGET FOR THE SQUARE FOOTAGE WE USE.

IT'S A FALSE SAVINGS! YOU'RE HURTING THE COMPANY!

ALL I HEAR IS A FAINT BUZZING.

OH, WELL. HOW BAD COULD IT BE?

I HOPE YOU LIKE BAKED BEANS AND SQUARE-DANCING AS MUCH AS I DO!

BEANS

© 1996 United Feature Syndicate, Inc. (NYC)

NOTES

NOTES

JANUARY 2000

JANUARY

S	M	T	W	T	F	S
						1
2	3	4	5	6	7	8
9	10	11	12	13	14	15
16	17	18	19	20	21	22
23	24	25	26	27	28	29
30	31					

3
MONDAY

4
TUESDAY

5
WEDNESDAY

6
THURSDAY

7
FRIDAY

8
SATURDAY

9
SUNDAY

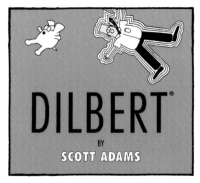

NOTES

NOTES

JANUARY 2000

JANUARY	S	M	T	W	T	F	S
							1
	2	3	4	5	6	7	8
	9	10	11	12	13	14	15
	16	17	18	19	20	21	22
	23	24	25	26	27	28	29
	30	31					

10
MONDAY

11
TUESDAY

12
WEDNESDAY

13
THURSDAY

14
FRIDAY

15
SATURDAY

16
SUNDAY

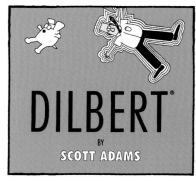

DILBERT
BY
SCOTT ADAMS

HEE HEE! THIS IS MY MOST DIABOLICAL WORK YET AS DIRECTOR OF HUMAN RESOURCES.

THANKS TO E-MAIL I CAN PLAY WITH HUNDREDS OF EMPLOYEES AT ONCE!

UH-OH... A MESSAGE FROM THE EVIL MISTER CATBERT.

"IN ORDER TO REDUCE OUR JANITORIAL EXPENSES..."

THAT'S A PHRASE YOU DON'T WANT TO SEE.

"EVERY ENGINEER WILL BE REQUIRED TO STRAP A BROOM TO HIS OR HER..."

"...BUTTOCKS."

ON THE POSITIVE SIDE, MARKETING INVITES US TO A LOT MORE MEETINGS NOW.

FIVE MINUTES; WE'RE STILL EATING COOKIES.

NOTES

NOTES

JANUARY 2000

JANUARY

S	M	T	W	T	F	S
						1
2	3	4	5	6	7	8
9	10	11	12	13	14	15
16	17	18	19	20	21	22
23	24	25	26	27	28	29
30	31					

17
MONDAY

MARTIN LUTHER KING JR.'S BIRTHDAY (OBSERVED)

18
TUESDAY

19
WEDNESDAY

20
THURSDAY

21
FRIDAY

22
SATURDAY

23
SUNDAY

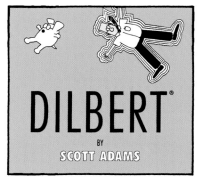

JANUARY 2000

S	M	T	W	T	F	S
JANUARY						1
2	3	4	5	6	7	8
9	10	11	12	13	14	15
16	17	18	19	20	21	22
23	24	25	26	27	28	29
30	31					

24 MONDAY

25 TUESDAY

26 WEDNESDAY

27 THURSDAY

28 FRIDAY

29 SATURDAY

30 SUNDAY

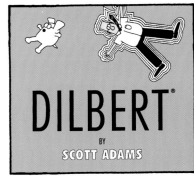

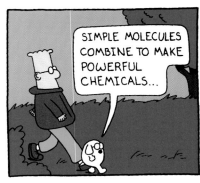

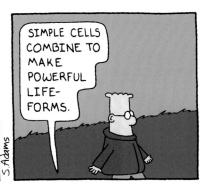

NOTES

NOTES

JAN-FEB 2000

JANUARY	S	M	T	W	T	F	S
							1
	2	3	4	5	6	7	8
	9	10	11	12	13	14	15
	16	17	18	19	20	21	22
	23	24	25	26	27	28	29
	30	31					

FEBRUARY	S	M	T	W	T	F	S
			1	2	3	4	5
	6	7	8	9	10	11	12
	13	14	15	16	17	18	19
	20	21	22	23	24	25	26
	27	28	29				

31 MONDAY

1 TUESDAY

2 WEDNESDAY
Groundhog Day

3 THURSDAY

4 FRIDAY

5 SATURDAY

6 SUNDAY

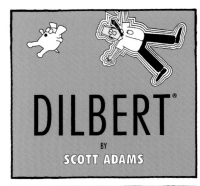

NOTES

NOTES

FEBRUARY 2000

FEBRUARY

S	M	T	W	T	F	S
		1	2	3	4	5
6	7	8	9	10	11	12
13	14	15	16	17	18	19
20	21	22	23	24	25	26
27	28	29				

7
MONDAY

8
TUESDAY

9
WEDNESDAY

10
THURSDAY

11
FRIDAY

12
SATURDAY

13
SUNDAY

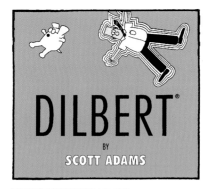

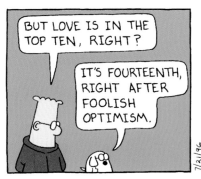

NOTES

NOTES

FEBRUARY 2000

FEBRUARY

S	M	T	W	T	F	S
		1	2	3	4	5
6	7	8	9	10	11	12
13	14	15	16	17	18	19
20	21	22	23	24	25	26
27	28	29				

14 MONDAY
VALENTINE'S DAY

15 TUESDAY

16 WEDNESDAY

17 THURSDAY

18 FRIDAY

19 SATURDAY

20 SUNDAY

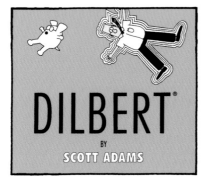

DILBERT®

BY
SCOTT ADAMS

I'M EMBARRASSED TO WORK AT MY COMPANY, DOGBERT.

WE CAN'T EVEN PAY A SIMPLE INVOICE IN LESS THAN SIX MONTHS.

"FIRST IT COMES TO OUR MAIL ROOM FOR AGING."

DO WE LIKE DILBERT?

BAD HAIRCUT. PENALTY BOX.

PENALTY BOX

"MONTHS LATER IT GETS TO OUR DEPARTMENT SECRETARY."

IT'S URGENT.

I'LL START IGNORING IT IMMEDIATELY.

"EVENTUALLY MY BOSS GETS IT. HE USES IT TO DEMONSTRATE HIS INABILITY TO GRASP THE CONCEPT OF TIME."

LET'S GET SOME MORE BIDS.

THAT WAS THE PAST. THIS IS THE PRESENT.

"IF IT MAKES IT TO THE ACCOUNTS PAYABLE GROUP, IT WILL BE EATEN BY TROLLS."

NO, THANKS. I'M FULL.

JUST A TASTE.

HOW WOULD YOU PROTECT YOUR REPUTATION IF YOU WERE ASSOCIATED WITH SOMETHING SO PATHETIC?

I'D TELL EVERYBODY THAT THE DOOFY GUY IS MY BUTLER.

HYPOTHETICALLY.

© 1996 United Feature Syndicate, Inc. (NYC)

NOTES

NOTES

FEBRUARY 2000

FEBRUARY

S	M	T	W	T	F	S
		1	2	3	4	5
6	7	8	9	10	11	12
13	14	15	16	17	18	19
20	21	22	23	24	25	26
27	28	29				

21 MONDAY

Presidents' Day

22 TUESDAY

23 WEDNESDAY

24 THURSDAY

25 FRIDAY

26 SATURDAY

27 SUNDAY

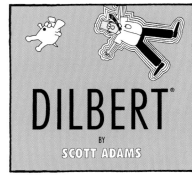

DILBERT

BY SCOTT ADAMS

I WANT YOU TO INTERVIEW THE NEW CANDIDATE FOR ENGINEERING. DON'T REVEAL ANY UGLY TRUTHS.

AT THIS COMPANY WE'RE DEDICATED TO THE PRINCIPLE OF EMPLOYEE EMPOWERMENT, JENNIFER.

THE "PRINCIPLE OF EMPLOYEE EMPOWER-MENT"?

UH-OH.

WHY WOULD YOU HAVE A SPECIAL PHRASE FOR SOMETHING LIKE THAT?

IF YOU COULD REALLY MAKE DECISIONS ON YOUR OWN IT WOULD NEVER OCCUR TO YOU TO INVENT A PHRASE FOR IT.

MY SHIELDS ARE DOWN... A HULL BREACH IS IMMINENT...

JUST DON'T TELL ME YOU HAVE "QUALITY TEAMS".

RUN FOR IT, JENNIFER!!! IT'S TOO LATE FOR ME BUT YOU CAN SAVE YOURSELF!!! RUN!!!

WHOA! HULL BREACH. ANY SURVIVORS?

ONE. I HAD TO JETTISON MY DIGNITY BUT SHE MADE IT TO THE ESCAPE POD.

NOTES

NOTES

FEB-MAR 2000

FEBRUARY

S	M	T	W	T	F	S
		1	2	3	4	5
6	7	8	9	10	11	12
13	14	15	16	17	18	19
20	21	22	23	24	25	26
27	28	29				

MARCH

S	M	T	W	T	F	S
			1	2	3	4
5	6	7	8	9	10	11
12	13	14	15	16	17	18
19	20	21	22	23	24	25
26	27	28	29	30	31	

28 MONDAY

29 TUESDAY

1 WEDNESDAY

2 THURSDAY

3 FRIDAY

4 SATURDAY

5 SUNDAY

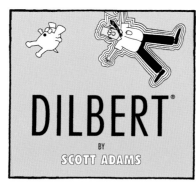

DILBERT®

BY SCOTT ADAMS

MYSTERIES REVEALED

HOW DO CEILING TILES GET DAMAGED?

IT BEGINS WITH A LOWLY ENGINEER WHO MAKES A TECHNOLOGY DECISION.

THE ENGINEER WRITES UP HIS RECOMMENDATION.

TEN PAGES.

THE BOSS SUMMARIZES IT FOR THE EXECUTIVE DIRECTOR.

ONE-PAGE SUMMARY.

THE EXECUTIVE DIRECTOR SUMMARIZES IT FOR THE VICE PRESIDENT.

THREE BULLET POINTS...

THE VP SUMMARIZES IT FOR THE PRESIDENT.

NICE NECKTIE.

THANKS. HAVE SOME STOCK OPTIONS.

THE PRESIDENT SEES A CNN REPORT AND MAKES A TECHNOLOGY DECISION.

INTERACTIVE HOLOGRAPHS ARE HOT!

GET ME SOME OF THAT!

THE ENGINEER IS ASSIGNED TO JUSTIFY THE PRESIDENT'S TECHNOLOGY DECISION.

HE TOOK THAT WELL.

OUCH

© 1996 United Feature Syndicate, Inc. (NYC)

NOTES

NOTES

MARCH 2000

MARCH

S	M	T	W	T	F	S
			1	2	3	4
5	6	7	8	9	10	11
12	13	14	15	16	17	18
19	20	21	22	23	24	25
26	27	28	29	30	31	

6 MONDAY

7 TUESDAY

8 WEDNESDAY
ASH WEDNESDAY

9 THURSDAY

10 FRIDAY

11 SATURDAY

12 SUNDAY

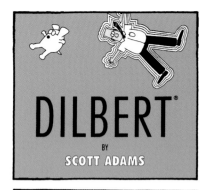

MARCH 2000

	S	M	T	W	T	F	S
MARCH				1	2	3	4
	5	6	7	8	9	10	11
	12	13	14	15	16	17	18
	19	20	21	22	23	24	25
	26	27	28	29	30	31	

13 MONDAY

14 TUESDAY

15 WEDNESDAY

16 THURSDAY

17 FRIDAY
St. Patrick's Day

18 SATURDAY

19 SUNDAY

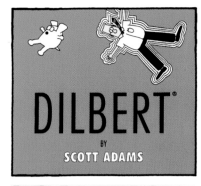

DILBERT
BY
SCOTT ADAMS

NOTES

NOTES

MARCH 2000

MARCH

S	M	T	W	T	F	S
			1	2	3	4
5	6	7	8	9	10	11
12	13	14	15	16	17	18
19	20	21	22	23	24	25
26	27	28	29	30	31	

20 MONDAY

21 TUESDAY
Purim

22 WEDNESDAY

23 THURSDAY

24 FRIDAY

25 SATURDAY

26 SUNDAY

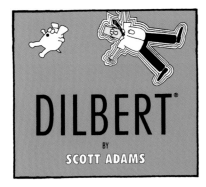

NOTES

NOTES

MAR-APR 2000

MARCH

S	M	T	W	T	F	S
			1	2	3	4
5	6	7	8	9	10	11
12	13	14	15	16	17	18
19	20	21	22	23	24	25
26	27	28	29	30	31	

APRIL

S	M	T	W	T	F	S
						1
2	3	4	5	6	7	8
9	10	11	12	13	14	15
16	17	18	19	20	21	22
23	24	25	26	27	28	29
30						

27 MONDAY

28 TUESDAY

29 WEDNESDAY

30 THURSDAY

31 FRIDAY

1 SATURDAY

2 SUNDAY

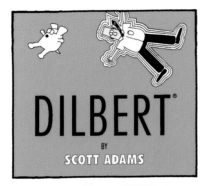

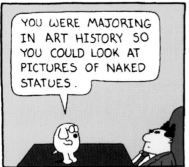

APRIL 2000

APRIL

S	M	T	W	T	F	S
						1
2	3	4	5	6	7	8
9	10	11	12	13	14	15
16	17	18	19	20	21	22
23	24	25	26	27	28	29
30						

3 MONDAY

4 TUESDAY

5 WEDNESDAY

6 THURSDAY

7 FRIDAY

8 SATURDAY

9 SUNDAY

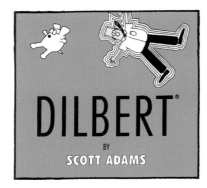

APRIL 2000

APRIL

S	M	T	W	T	F	S
						1
2	3	4	5	6	7	8
9	10	11	12	13	14	15
16	17	18	19	20	21	22
23	24	25	26	27	28	29
30						

10
MONDAY

11
TUESDAY

12
WEDNESDAY

13
THURSDAY

14
FRIDAY

15
SATURDAY

16
SUNDAY

PALM SUNDAY

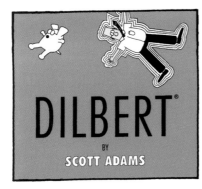

NOTES

NOTES

APRIL 2000

	S	M	T	W	T	F	S
APRIL							1
	2	3	4	5	6	7	8
	9	10	11	12	13	14	15
	16	17	18	19	20	21	22
	23	24	25	26	27	28	29
	30						

17 MONDAY

18 TUESDAY

19 WEDNESDAY

20 THURSDAY
Passover

21 FRIDAY
Good Friday

22 SATURDAY

23 SUNDAY
Easter

DILBERT

BY
SCOTT ADAMS

NOTES

NOTES

APRIL 2000

	S	M	T	W	T	F	S
APRIL							1
	2	3	4	5	6	7	8
	9	10	11	12	13	14	15
	16	17	18	19	20	21	22
	23	24	25	26	27	28	29
	30						

24 MONDAY
Easter Monday (Canada)

25 TUESDAY

26 WEDNESDAY
Secretaries Day

27 THURSDAY

28 FRIDAY

29 SATURDAY

30 SUNDAY

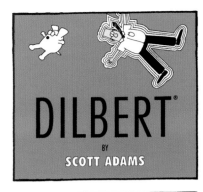

DILBERT®
BY
SCOTT ADAMS

I NEED TO MOVE YOU ONE CUBICLE DOWN.

WHY?

THAT WAY MY PEOPLE WILL BE IN A SQUARE PATTERN.

YOU'RE IN A RANDOM PATTERN NOW. THE SYMMETRY IS BAD.

YOU WANT ME TO WASTE TWO DAYS OF WORK TO MOVE...

I'LL HAVE NO PHONE AND NO NETWORK CONNECTION FOR A WEEK...

I'LL HAVE TO ORDER NEW BUSINESS CARDS AND UPDATE MY CUBICLE ADDRESS ON DOZENS OF RECORDS.

AND YOU STILL WON'T HAVE A **SQUARE** BECAUSE THERE ARE **FIVE** OF US.

I GOT DOWNSIZED. APPARENTLY SOMEBODY COMPLAINED THAT I FORMED A PENTAGON.

THAT CAN HAPPEN.

© 1996 United Feature Syndicate, Inc.

NOTES

NOTES

MAY 2000

MAY

S	M	T	W	T	F	S
	1	2	3	4	5	6
7	8	9	10	11	12	13
14	15	16	17	18	19	20
21	22	23	24	25	26	27
28	29	30	31			

1
MONDAY

2
TUESDAY

3
WEDNESDAY

4
THURSDAY

5
FRIDAY

6
SATURDAY

7
SUNDAY

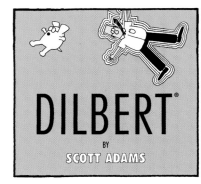

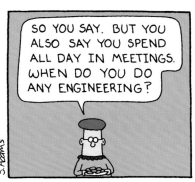

NOTES

NOTES

MAY 2000

MAY

S	M	T	W	T	F	S
	1	2	3	4	5	6
7	8	9	10	11	12	13
14	15	16	17	18	19	20
21	22	23	24	25	26	27
28	29	30	31			

8
MONDAY

9
TUESDAY

10
WEDNESDAY

11
THURSDAY

12
FRIDAY

13
SATURDAY

14
SUNDAY

MOTHER'S DAY

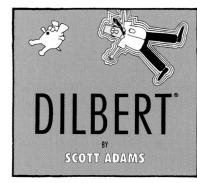

DILBERT
BY
SCOTT ADAMS

I'D LIKE YOU ALL TO MEET OUR NEW VICE PRESIDENT IN CHARGE OF COST CONTAINMENT.

MY FIRST PRIORITY IS TO REDUCE OUR SPIRALING EXPENSES FOR OFFICE SUPPLIES.

FROM NOW ON, YOUR SUPPLY CABINET WILL BE LOCKED.

THE ONLY KEY WILL BE UNDER THE CONTROL OF YOUR BITTER AND INEFFICIENT SECRETARY.

QUESTIONS?

I AM ONLY AN INTERN SO PLEASE EXCUSE THIS NAIVE QUESTION...

I'VE NOTICED THAT THE EMPLOYEES ARE ALL DISPIRITED HOLLOW SHELLS, MANAGEMENT IS RANDOM AND OUR PRODUCTS ARE SHODDY.

HOW ARE YOU GOING TO SOLVE THAT BY MAKING IT HARD TO GET SUPPLIES?

I THOUGHT YOU SAID THEY LIKE HONESTY.

ASK HOW MUCH HE'S PAID. IT SHOWS YOU CARE.

NOTES

NOTES

MAY 2000

MAY

	S	M	T	W	T	F	S
		1	2	3	4	5	6
	7	8	9	10	11	12	13
	14	15	16	17	18	19	20
	21	22	23	24	25	26	27
	28	29	30	31			

15 MONDAY

16 TUESDAY

17 WEDNESDAY

18 THURSDAY

19 FRIDAY

20 SATURDAY

ARMED FORCES DAY

21 SUNDAY

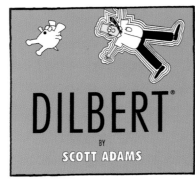

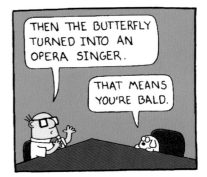

NOTES

NOTES

MAY 2000

MAY

S	M	T	W	T	F	S
	1	2	3	4	5	6
7	8	9	10	11	12	13
14	15	16	17	18	19	20
21	22	23	24	25	26	27
28	29	30	31			

22 MONDAY

Victoria Day (Canada)

23 TUESDAY

24 WEDNESDAY

25 THURSDAY

26 FRIDAY

27 SATURDAY

28 SUNDAY

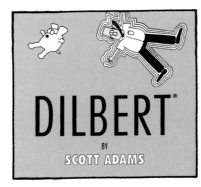

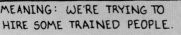

MAY–JUNE 2000

MAY	S	M	T	W	T	F	S
		1	2	3	4	5	6
	7	8	9	10	11	12	13
	14	15	16	17	18	19	20
	21	22	23	24	25	26	27
	28	29	30	31			

JUNE	S	M	T	W	T	F	S
					1	2	3
	4	5	6	7	8	9	10
	11	12	13	14	15	16	17
	18	19	20	21	22	23	24
	25	26	27	28	29	30	

29 MONDAY
MEMORIAL DAY

30 TUESDAY

31 WEDNESDAY

1 THURSDAY

2 FRIDAY

3 SATURDAY

4 SUNDAY

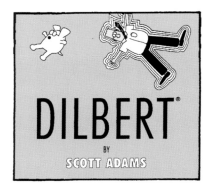

© 1996 United Feature Syndicate, Inc.

NOTES

_____

_____

_____

_____

_____

_____

_____

NOTES

JUNE 2000

JUNE

S	M	T	W	T	F	S
				1	2	3
4	5	6	7	8	9	10
11	12	13	14	15	16	17
18	19	20	21	22	23	24
25	26	27	28	29	30	

5
MONDAY

6
TUESDAY

7
WEDNESDAY

8
THURSDAY

9
FRIDAY

10
SATURDAY

11
SUNDAY

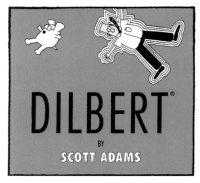

DILBERT
BY
SCOTT ADAMS

I'LL BE WRITING YOUR PERFORMANCE REVIEW THIS AFTERNOON.

BUT THIS MORNING I'M HELPING MY DAUGHTER SELL CUB GIRL COOKIES.

FOR YOUR SHOPPING CONVENIENCE I HAVE ASSIGNED A NAME TO EACH VOLUME LEVEL.

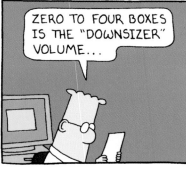

ZERO TO FOUR BOXES IS THE "DOWNSIZER" VOLUME...

FIVE TO EIGHT BOXES IS THE "LOW PERFORMER" VOLUME LEVEL.

LET'S SAY SIX HUNDRED BOXES.

AHH... THE "FAST TRACKER." AN EXCELLENT CHOICE.

WHAT'S YOUR DAUGHTER'S NAME?

OOH... GOTTA GO.

I ONLY BOUGHT TWELVE BOXES. NOW I'M THE "UNITED WAY" CHAIRPERSON.

I JUST SIGNED YOUR NAME FOR SIX HUNDRED MORE.

© 1996 United Feature Syndicate, Inc.

7/7/96

NOTES

NOTES

JUNE 2000

JUNE

S	M	T	W	T	F	S
				1	2	3
4	5	6	7	8	9	10
11	12	13	14	15	16	17
18	19	20	21	22	23	24
25	26	27	28	29	30	

12 MONDAY

13 TUESDAY

14 WEDNESDAY
Flag Day

15 THURSDAY

16 FRIDAY

17 SATURDAY

18 SUNDAY
Father's Day

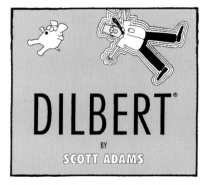

DILBERT
BY
SCOTT ADAMS

DILBERT, I'VE DECIDED TO DOWNSIZE YOU.

IT'S NOTHING PERSONAL, JUST AN ECONOMIC NECESSITY.

I CALCULATED HOW MUCH YOUR SALARY WAS DRAGGING DOWN THE VALUE OF MY STOCK OPTIONS.

WITHOUT YOU, I CAN AFFORD TO GO TO THE MOVIES ONE ADDITIONAL TIME PER YEAR.

AND LET'S FACE IT: RECREATION IS IMPORTANT WHEN ONE HAS A STRESSFUL JOB.

HEY, WHY DON'T YOU DOWNSIZE WALLY INSTEAD. YOU'LL SAVE ENOUGH IN OFFICE SUPPLIES TO BUY POPCORN TOO.

SHEESH!

MMM...

HOW'D IT GO?

YOU KNOW THAT TEAM-BUILDING EXERCISE WE DID LAST WEEK?

IT DIDN'T TAKE.

NOTES

NOTES

JUNE 2000

JUNE

S	M	T	W	T	F	S
				1	2	3
4	5	6	7	8	9	10
11	12	13	14	15	16	17
18	19	20	21	22	23	24
25	26	27	28	29	30	

19 MONDAY

20 TUESDAY

21 WEDNESDAY

22 THURSDAY

23 FRIDAY

24 SATURDAY

25 SUNDAY

NOTES

NOTES

JUNE-JULY 2000

JUNE

S	M	T	W	T	F	S
				1	2	3
4	5	6	7	8	9	10
11	12	13	14	15	16	17
18	19	20	21	22	23	24
25	26	27	28	29	30	

JULY

S	M	T	W	T	F	S
						1
2	3	4	5	6	7	8
9	10	11	12	13	14	15
16	17	18	19	20	21	22
23	24	25	26	27	28	29
30	31					

26 MONDAY

27 TUESDAY

28 WEDNESDAY

29 THURSDAY

30 FRIDAY

1 SATURDAY
Canada Day

2 SUNDAY

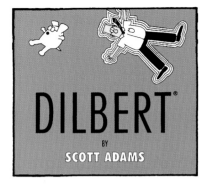

NOTES

NOTES

JULY 2000

JULY

S	M	T	W	T	F	S
						1
2	3	4	5	6	7	8
9	10	11	12	13	14	15
16	17	18	19	20	21	22
23	24	25	26	27	28	29
30	31					

3 MONDAY

4 TUESDAY
INDEPENDENCE DAY

5 WEDNESDAY

6 THURSDAY

7 FRIDAY

8 SATURDAY

9 SUNDAY

DILBERT
BY
SCOTT ADAMS

© 1996 United Feature Syndicate, Inc.

NOTES

NOTES

JULY 2000

JULY

S	M	T	W	T	F	S
						1
2	3	4	5	6	7	8
9	10	11	12	13	14	15
16	17	18	19	20	21	22
23	24	25	26	27	28	29
30	31					

10 MONDAY

11 TUESDAY

12 WEDNESDAY

13 THURSDAY

14 FRIDAY

15 SATURDAY

16 SUNDAY

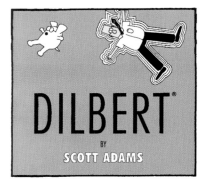

DILBERT

BY

SCOTT ADAMS

THE BUDGET TRAP

I NEED A QUICK ESTIMATE FOR HOW MUCH YOUR NEXT PROJECT WILL COST, WALLY.

HOW SHOULD I KNOW? YOU HAVEN'T EVEN TOLD ME WHAT MY NEXT PROJECT IS.

THAT'S OKAY. I ONLY NEED A ROUGH ESTIMATE FOR PLANNING PURPOSES.

I SEE WHERE THIS IS GOING. YOU'RE GOING TO TURN MY WILD GUESS INTO A BUDGET. LATER I'LL BE BLAMED WHEN IT'S WRONG.

NO, NO. I WON'T HOLD YOU TO THESE NUMBERS.

WELL...OKAY, LET'S SAY TWO MILLION DOLLARS.

OOH...CAN'T AFFORD THAT. I'LL PUT YOU DOWN FOR TWENTY THOUSAND DOLLARS.

ONE YEAR LATER...

YOU'RE WAY OVER BUDGET. CAN YOU SHOW ME THE CAUSE?

IT DEPENDS. CAN MIRRORS REFLECT YOUR IMAGE?

NOTES

NOTES

JULY 2000

JULY

S	M	T	W	T	F	S
						1
2	3	4	5	6	7	8
9	10	11	12	13	14	15
16	17	18	19	20	21	22
23	24	25	26	27	28	29
30	31					

17 MONDAY

18 TUESDAY

19 WEDNESDAY

20 THURSDAY

21 FRIDAY

22 SATURDAY

23 SUNDAY

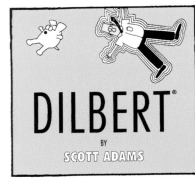

JULY 2000

JULY

S	M	T	W	T	F	S
						1
2	3	4	5	6	7	8
9	10	11	12	13	14	15
16	17	18	19	20	21	22
23	24	25	26	27	28	29
30	31					

24
MONDAY

25
TUESDAY

26
WEDNESDAY

27
THURSDAY

28
FRIDAY

29
SATURDAY

30
SUNDAY

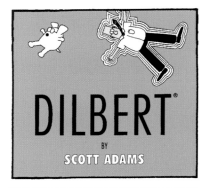

DILBERT

BY
SCOTT ADAMS

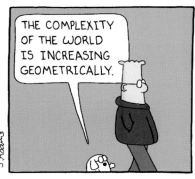

NOTES

NOTES

JULY–AUG 2000

JULY

S	M	T	W	T	F	S
						1
2	3	4	5	6	7	8
9	10	11	12	13	14	15
16	17	18	19	20	21	22
23	24	25	26	27	28	29
30	31					

AUGUST

S	M	T	W	T	F	S
		1	2	3	4	5
6	7	8	9	10	11	12
13	14	15	16	17	18	19
20	21	22	23	24	25	26
27	28	29	30	31		

31 MONDAY

1 TUESDAY

2 WEDNESDAY

3 THURSDAY

4 FRIDAY

5 SATURDAY

6 SUNDAY

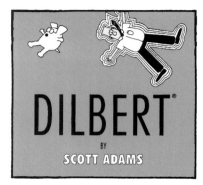

AUGUST 2000

AUGUST

S	M	T	W	T	F	S
		1	2	3	4	5
6	7	8	9	10	11	12
13	14	15	16	17	18	19
20	21	22	23	24	25	26
27	28	29	30	31		

7 MONDAY

8 TUESDAY

9 WEDNESDAY

10 THURSDAY

11 FRIDAY

12 SATURDAY

13 SUNDAY

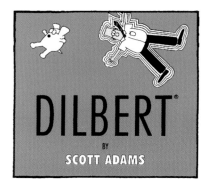

DILBERT
BY
SCOTT ADAMS

NOTES

NOTES

AUGUST 2000

AUGUST

S	M	T	W	T	F	S
		1	2	3	4	5
6	7	8	9	10	11	12
13	14	15	16	17	18	19
20	21	22	23	24	25	26
27	28	29	30	31		

14 MONDAY

15 TUESDAY

16 WEDNESDAY

17 THURSDAY

18 FRIDAY

19 SATURDAY

20 SUNDAY

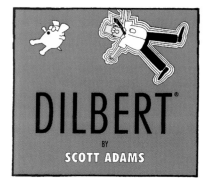

NOTES

NOTES

AUGUST 2000

AUGUST

S	M	T	W	T	F	S
		1	2	3	4	5
6	7	8	9	10	11	12
13	14	15	16	17	18	19
20	21	22	23	24	25	26
27	28	29	30	31		

21 MONDAY

22 TUESDAY

23 WEDNESDAY

24 THURSDAY

25 FRIDAY

26 SATURDAY

27 SUNDAY

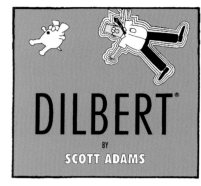

AUG-SEPT 2000

AUGUST

S	M	T	W	T	F	S
		1	2	3	4	5
6	7	8	9	10	11	12
13	14	15	16	17	18	19
20	21	22	23	24	25	26
27	28	29	30	31		

SEPTEMBER

S	M	T	W	T	F	S
					1	2
3	4	5	6	7	8	9
10	11	12	13	14	15	16
17	18	19	20	21	22	23
24	25	26	27	28	29	30

28 MONDAY

29 TUESDAY

30 WEDNESDAY

31 THURSDAY

1 FRIDAY

2 SATURDAY

3 SUNDAY

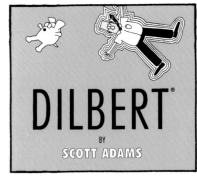

NOTES

NOTES

SEPTEMBER 2000

SEPTEMBER

S	M	T	W	T	F	S
					1	2
3	4	5	6	7	8	9
10	11	12	13	14	15	16
17	18	19	20	21	22	23
24	25	26	27	28	29	30

4
MONDAY
Labor Day

5
TUESDAY

6
WEDNESDAY

7
THURSDAY

8
FRIDAY

9
SATURDAY

10
SUNDAY

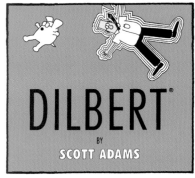

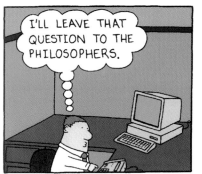

SEPTEMBER 2000

SEPTEMBER

S	M	T	W	T	F	S
					1	2
3	4	5	6	7	8	9
10	11	12	13	14	15	16
17	18	19	20	21	22	23
24	25	26	27	28	29	30

11
MONDAY

12
TUESDAY

13
WEDNESDAY

14
THURSDAY

15
FRIDAY

16
SATURDAY

17
SUNDAY

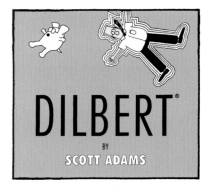

NOTES

NOTES

SEPTEMBER 2000

SEPTEMBER

S	M	T	W	T	F	S
					1	2
3	4	5	6	7	8	9
10	11	12	13	14	15	16
17	18	19	20	21	22	23
24	25	26	27	28	29	30

18 MONDAY

19 TUESDAY

20 WEDNESDAY

21 THURSDAY

22 FRIDAY

23 SATURDAY

24 SUNDAY

DILBERT

BY SCOTT ADAMS

NOBODY HAS NOMINATED A CO-WORKER FOR A SPECIAL ACHIEVEMENT AWARD.

SOMEONE IN THIS GROUP MUST HAVE DONE **SOMETHING** GOOD THIS YEAR.

NO... I DON'T THINK SO.

WE'D REMEMBER SOMETHING LIKE THAT.

THIS LOOKS BAD. ALL THE OTHER DEPARTMENTS ARE GIVING THEMSELVES AWARDS.

WE MIGHT HAVE TO LOWER OUR STANDARDS A BIT.

I'VE BEEN PROACTIVE IN THAT AREA.

WHY ARE WE STANDING IN THE HALLWAY?

WE THINK THE ROOM IS LOCKED.

WE DON'T HAVE THE KEY.

© 1996 United Feature Syndicate, Inc.

LATER THAT MONTH

THIS AWARD GOES TO ALICE FOR BOLDLY TRYING THE DOOR KNOB.

WHEN I FIND OUT WHO NOMINATED ME...

NOTES

NOTES

SEPT-OCT 2000

25 MONDAY

26 TUESDAY

27 WEDNESDAY

28 THURSDAY

29 FRIDAY

30 SATURDAY

Rosh Hashanah

1 SUNDAY

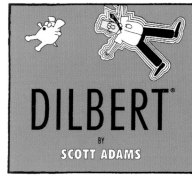

DILBERT

BY

SCOTT ADAMS

ALICE, YOUR PERFORMANCE THIS YEAR IS "MEETS EXPECTATIONS." YOU GET A TWO PERCENT RAISE.

MEETS EXPECTATIONS?! I WORKED EIGHTY HOURS EVERY WEEK!

YEAH... WELL, I EXPECTED THAT.

I EARNED THREE PATENTS THIS YEAR! THE COMPANY WILL MAKE MILLIONS!!

REALLY? WOW.

I MEAN... I EXPECTED THAT TOO.

I DONATED BONE MARROW TO OUR BIGGEST CUSTOMER!!!

TWICE!!!

I NOTED THAT UNDER "ATTENDANCE PROBLEM."

I TOLD YOU THE BONE MARROW THING WOULD HAUNT YOU.

I'M STARTING TO THINK THE TIME I WORKED THROUGH LUNCH WAS FOR NOTHING.

© 1996 United Feature Syndicate, Inc.

NOTES

NOTES

OCTOBER 2000

OCTOBER

S	M	T	W	T	F	S
1	2	3	4	5	6	7
8	9	10	11	12	13	14
15	16	17	18	19	20	21
22	23	24	25	26	27	28
29	30	31				

2
MONDAY

3
TUESDAY

4
WEDNESDAY

5
THURSDAY

6
FRIDAY

7
SATURDAY

8
SUNDAY

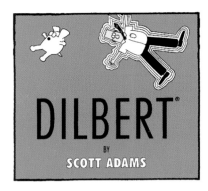

DILBERT
BY
SCOTT ADAMS

MY PROJECT IS RIGHT ON PLAN.

IT BEGAN LAST WEEK AS A BAD IDEA FROM SOMEBODY IN SENIOR MANAGEMENT.

THANKS TO MY LEADERSHIP, IT IS ALREADY AN OBJECT OF WIDESPREAD MOCKERY AND DERISION.

AS I SPEAK, OUR LAWYERS ARE PURGING EVERY LAST TRACE OF VALUE IT MIGHT HAVE HAD.

WITH LUCK, THE PROJECT WILL BE A GIGANTIC FAILURE IN A MONTH.

PEOPLE WILL FORGET MY FAILURE AND REMEMBER THAT I'M EXPERIENCED. PROMOTIONS WILL FOLLOW.

YES!!

IN SIX MONTHS I'LL BE DATING AN EXECUTIVE SECRETARY NAMED YVONNE.

GOOD PLAN.

WALLY, HAVE YOU EVER READ OUR MISSION STATEMENT?

YEAH, BUT I DON'T SUBSCRIBE TO A LITERAL INTERPRETATION.

© 1996 United Feature Syndicate, Inc.

NOTES

NOTES

OCTOBER 2000

OCTOBER

S	M	T	W	T	F	S
1	2	3	4	5	6	7
8	9	10	11	12	13	14
15	16	17	18	19	20	21
22	23	24	25	26	27	28
29	30	31				

9 MONDAY
Columbus Day • Yom Kippur • Thanksgiving (Canada)

10 TUESDAY

11 WEDNESDAY

12 THURSDAY

13 FRIDAY

14 SATURDAY

15 SUNDAY

NOTES

NOTES

OCTOBER 2000

OCTOBER

S M T W T F S
1 2 3 4 5 6 7
8 9 10 11 12 13 14
15 16 17 18 19 20 21
22 23 24 25 26 27 28
29 30 31

16 MONDAY
National Boss Day

17 TUESDAY

18 WEDNESDAY

19 THURSDAY

20 FRIDAY

21 SATURDAY

22 SUNDAY

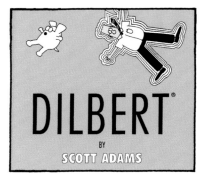

NOTES

NOTES

OCTOBER 2000

OCTOBER

S	M	T	W	T	F	S
1	2	3	4	5	6	7
8	9	10	11	12	13	14
15	16	17	18	19	20	21
22	23	24	25	26	27	28
29	30	31				

23
MONDAY

24
TUESDAY

25
WEDNESDAY

26
THURSDAY

27
FRIDAY

28
SATURDAY

29
SUNDAY

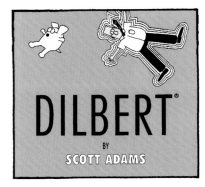

DILBERT
BY
SCOTT ADAMS

MY NEXT VICTIM.

I AM PHIL, THE PRINCE OF INSUFFICIENT LIGHT AND SUPREME RULER OF HECK!!

HI, PHIL.

YOU MUST CHOOSE ONE OF THESE TWO HIDEOUS FATES TO PAY FOR YOUR SINS.

YOU CAN CHOOSE ETERNAL HIGH PAY, BUT ALL OF YOUR WORK WILL BE BURNED IN FRONT OF YOU AT THE END OF EACH DAY...

OR YOU CAN CHOOSE ETERNAL POVERTY, BUT YOUR WORK WILL BE USEFUL AND APPRECIATED.

WOW! THEY'RE BOTH BETTER THAN MY CURRENT JOB!

HEY, WALLY, YOU MIGHT WANT TO GET IN ON THIS!

© 1996 United Feature Syndicate, Inc.

6/2/96

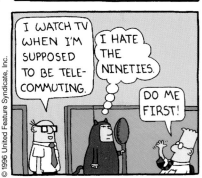

I WATCH TV WHEN I'M SUPPOSED TO BE TELE-COMMUTING.

I HATE THE NINETIES.

DO ME FIRST!

NOTES

NOTES

OCT-NOV 2000

OCTOBER

S	M	T	W	T	F	S
1	2	3	4	5	6	7
8	9	10	11	12	13	14
15	16	17	18	19	20	21
22	23	24	25	26	27	28
29	30	31				

NOVEMBER

S	M	T	W	T	F	S
			1	2	3	4
5	6	7	8	9	10	11
12	13	14	15	16	17	18
19	20	21	22	23	24	25
26	27	28	29	30		

30 MONDAY

31 TUESDAY
HALLOWEEN

1 WEDNESDAY

2 THURSDAY

3 FRIDAY

4 SATURDAY

5 SUNDAY

DILBERT

BY SCOTT ADAMS

I'VE BEEN OFFERED A PROMOTION IN ANOTHER DEPARTMENT.

FANTASY

I'M OUTTA HERE, YOU WORTHLESS PIECE OF SNAIL CRUD!!

HA HA HA HA HA HA!!!

REALITY

I MEEKLY REQUEST TO BE RELEASED FROM MY CURRENT ASSIGNMENT.

FANTASY

I WOULD NEVER STAND IN YOUR WAY.

CONGRATULATIONS!

REALITY

I CAN'T RELEASE YOU. YOU'RE TOO VALUABLE.

FANTASY

IF I'M SO VALUABLE, EXPLAIN MY LAST RAISE!!!

REALITY

IN FACT, I HAVE **ANOTHER** VALUABLE ASSIGNMENT FOR YOU.

STUNNED SILENCE

11/10/96

© 1996 United Feature Syndicate, Inc.

I'M DOING A SURVEY TO FIND OUT WHY MORALE IS SO LOW.

I THINK IT'S YOUR BREATH.

NOTES

NOTES

NOVEMBER 2000

NOVEMBER

S	M	T	W	T	F	S
			1	2	3	4
5	6	7	8	9	10	11
12	13	14	15	16	17	18
19	20	21	22	23	24	25
26	27	28	29	30		

6 MONDAY

7 TUESDAY
Election Day

8 WEDNESDAY

9 THURSDAY

10 FRIDAY

11 SATURDAY
Veterans' Day • Remembrance Day (Canada)

12 SUNDAY

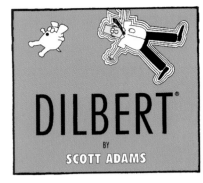

DILBERT
BY
SCOTT ADAMS

THE POWERFUL LEADER ENTERS CUBEVILLE TO INSPIRE THE WRETCHED UNDERLINGS.

HE SPOTS ONE OF THE LITTLE PEOPLE IN DESPERATE NEED OF A MORALE BOOST.

THE LEADER CAREFULLY ASSESSES THE SITUATION. EVERY SOLUTION IS UNIQUE.

TRY IDENTIFYING THE PROBLEM AND THEN SOLVING IT.

THE LEADER WAITS WHILE THE BRILLIANCE OF HIS CONTRIBUTION SINKS IN.

THAT'S A MUCH BETTER IDEA THAN WHAT I WAS DOING.

I'VE BEEN SITTING HERE ALL DAY RANDOMLY PRESSING KEYS. BUT YOU'VE SHOWN ME A BETTER WAY!

SUDDENLY THE LEADER REMEMBERS WHY HE RARELY VISITS CUBEVILLE.

MY MORALE IS SOARING.

NOTES

NOTES

NOVEMBER 2000

NOVEMBER

S	M	T	W	T	F	S
			1	2	3	4
5	6	7	8	9	10	11
12	13	14	15	16	17	18
19	20	21	22	23	24	25
26	27	28	29	30		

13 MONDAY

14 TUESDAY

15 WEDNESDAY

16 THURSDAY

17 FRIDAY

18 SATURDAY

19 SUNDAY

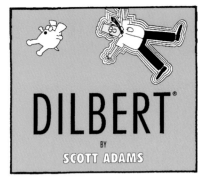

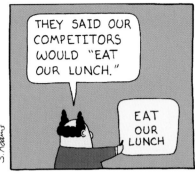

NOTES

NOTES

NOVEMBER 2000

NOVEMBER

S	M	T	W	T	F	S
			1	2	3	4
5	6	7	8	9	10	11
12	13	14	15	16	17	18
19	20	21	22	23	24	25
26	27	28	29	30		

20 MONDAY

21 TUESDAY

22 WEDNESDAY

23 THURSDAY
THANKSGIVING

24 FRIDAY

25 SATURDAY

26 SUNDAY

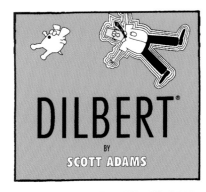

NOTES

NOTES

NOV-DEC 2000

NOVEMBER

S	M	T	W	T	F	S
			1	2	3	4
5	6	7	8	9	10	11
12	13	14	15	16	17	18
19	20	21	22	23	24	25
26	27	28	29	30		

DECEMBER

S	M	T	W	T	F	S
					1	2
3	4	5	6	7	8	9
10	11	12	13	14	15	16
17	18	19	20	21	22	23
24	25	26	27	28	29	30
31						

27 MONDAY

28 TUESDAY

29 WEDNESDAY

30 THURSDAY

1 FRIDAY

2 SATURDAY

3 SUNDAY

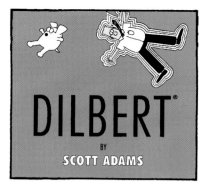

DILBERT

BY
SCOTT ADAMS

OUR POINTY-HAIRED BOSS WILL BE JOINING US BY SPEAKERPHONE.

THIS IS AN IMPORTANT PART OF YOUR ENGINEERING TRAINING, ASOK.

WHAT DO I DO?

WHEN ALICE PRESSES THE MUTE BUTTON, YOU MAKE WITTY AND SARCASTIC REMARKS.

RING RING

HELLO, EVERYONE. I'D LIKE TO TALK ABOUT THE NEW COMPENSATION PLAN.

TELL US SOME LIES, YOU UGLY, TWO-FACED, HYPOCRITICAL TROLL!

I AM ASOK THE INTERN AND I SPIT ON YOUR FEEBLE COMPENSATION PLAN!

I'VE FOUND STUFF ON THE BOTTOM OF MY SHOE THAT WAS SMARTER THAN YOU!! HA HA HA !!!

NEXT TIME, A BIT WITTIER... AND MAKE SURE ALICE REALLY PRESSES THE MUTE BUTTON.

NOTES

NOTES

DECEMBER 2000

	S	M	T	W	T	F	S
DECEMBER						1	2
	3	4	5	6	7	8	9
	10	11	12	13	14	15	16
	17	18	19	20	21	22	23
	24	25	26	27	28	29	30
	31						

4
MONDAY

5
TUESDAY

6
WEDNESDAY

7
THURSDAY

8
FRIDAY

9
SATURDAY

10
SUNDAY

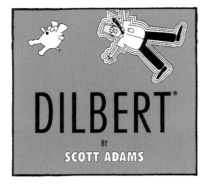

NOTES

NOTES

DECEMBER 2000

DECEMBER

S	M	T	W	T	F	S
					1	2
3	4	5	6	7	8	9
10	11	12	13	14	15	16
17	18	19	20	21	22	23
24	25	26	27	28	29	30
31						

11 MONDAY

12 TUESDAY

13 WEDNESDAY

14 THURSDAY

15 FRIDAY

16 SATURDAY

17 SUNDAY

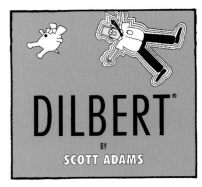

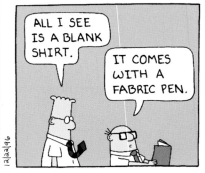

DECEMBER 2000

DECEMBER

S	M	T	W	T	F	S
					1	2
3	4	5	6	7	8	9
10	11	12	13	14	15	16
17	18	19	20	21	22	23
24	25	26	27	28	29	30
31						

18 MONDAY

19 TUESDAY

20 WEDNESDAY

21 THURSDAY

22 FRIDAY
HANUKKAH

23 SATURDAY

24 SUNDAY

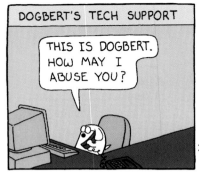

DECEMBER 2000

DECEMBER

S	M	T	W	T	F	S
					1	2
3	4	5	6	7	8	9
10	11	12	13	14	15	16
17	18	19	20	21	22	23
24	25	26	27	28	29	30
31						

25 MONDAY
Christmas

26 TUESDAY
Kwanzaa begins • Boxing Day (Canada)

27 WEDNESDAY

28 THURSDAY

29 FRIDAY

30 SATURDAY

31 SUNDAY

2001

JANUARY

_____

_____

FEBRUARY

_____

_____

MARCH

_____

_____

APRIL

_____

_____

MAY

_____

_____

JUNE

_____

_____

JULY

_____

_____

AUGUST

_____

_____

SEPTEMBER

_____

_____

OCTOBER

_____

_____

NOVEMBER

_____

_____

DECEMBER

_____

_____

1999

JANUARY
S	M	T	W	T	F	S
					1	2
3	4	5	6	7	8	9
10	11	12	13	14	15	16
17	18	19	20	21	22	23
24	25	26	27	28	29	30
31						

FEBRUARY
S	M	T	W	T	F	S
	1	2	3	4	5	6
7	8	9	10	11	12	13
14	15	16	17	18	19	20
21	22	23	24	25	26	27
28						

MARCH
S	M	T	W	T	F	S
	1	2	3	4	5	6
7	8	9	10	11	12	13
14	15	16	17	18	19	20
21	22	23	24	25	26	27
28	29	30	31			

APRIL
S	M	T	W	T	F	S
				1	2	3
4	5	6	7	8	9	10
11	12	13	14	15	16	17
18	19	20	21	22	23	24
25	26	27	28	29	30	

MAY
S	M	T	W	T	F	S
						1
2	3	4	5	6	7	8
9	10	11	12	13	14	15
16	17	18	19	20	21	22
23	24	25	26	27	28	29
30	31					

JUNE
S	M	T	W	T	F	S
		1	2	3	4	5
6	7	8	9	10	11	12
13	14	15	16	17	18	19
20	21	22	23	24	25	26
27	28	29	30			

JULY
S	M	T	W	T	F	S
				1	2	3
4	5	6	7	8	9	10
11	12	13	14	15	16	17
18	19	20	21	22	23	24
25	26	27	28	29	30	31

AUGUST
S	M	T	W	T	F	S
1	2	3	4	5	6	7
8	9	10	11	12	13	14
15	16	17	18	19	20	21
22	23	24	25	26	27	28
29	30	31				

SEPTEMBER
S	M	T	W	T	F	S
			1	2	3	4
5	6	7	8	9	10	11
12	13	14	15	16	17	18
19	20	21	22	23	24	25
26	27	28	29	30		

OCTOBER
S	M	T	W	T	F	S
					1	2
3	4	5	6	7	8	9
10	11	12	13	14	15	16
17	18	19	20	21	22	23
24	25	26	27	28	29	30
31						

NOVEMBER
S	M	T	W	T	F	S
	1	2	3	4	5	6
7	8	9	10	11	12	13
14	15	16	17	18	19	20
21	22	23	24	25	26	27
28	29	30				

DECEMBER
S	M	T	W	T	F	S
			1	2	3	4
5	6	7	8	9	10	11
12	13	14	15	16	17	18
19	20	21	22	23	24	25
26	27	28	29	30	31	

2001

JANUARY
S	M	T	W	T	F	S
	1	2	3	4	5	6
7	8	9	10	11	12	13
14	15	16	17	18	19	20
21	22	23	24	25	26	27
28	29	30	31			

FEBRUARY
S	M	T	W	T	F	S
				1	2	3
4	5	6	7	8	9	10
11	12	13	14	15	16	17
18	19	20	21	22	23	24
25	26	27	28			

MARCH
S	M	T	W	T	F	S
				1	2	3
4	5	6	7	8	9	10
11	12	13	14	15	16	17
18	19	20	21	22	23	24
25	26	27	28	29	30	31

APRIL
S	M	T	W	T	F	S
1	2	3	4	5	6	7
8	9	10	11	12	13	14
15	16	17	18	19	20	21
22	23	24	25	26	27	28
29	30					

MAY
S	M	T	W	T	F	S
		1	2	3	4	5
6	7	8	9	10	11	12
13	14	15	16	17	18	19
20	21	22	23	24	25	26
27	28	29	30	31		

JUNE
S	M	T	W	T	F	S
					1	2
3	4	5	6	7	8	9
10	11	12	13	14	15	16
17	18	19	20	21	22	23
24	25	26	27	28	29	30

JULY
S	M	T	W	T	F	S
1	2	3	4	5	6	7
8	9	10	11	12	13	14
15	16	17	18	19	20	21
22	23	24	25	26	27	28
29	30	31				

AUGUST
S	M	T	W	T	F	S
			1	2	3	4
5	6	7	8	9	10	11
12	13	14	15	16	17	18
19	20	21	22	23	24	25
26	27	28	29	30	31	

SEPTEMBER
S	M	T	W	T	F	S
						1
2	3	4	5	6	7	8
9	10	11	12	13	14	15
16	17	18	19	20	21	22
23	24	25	26	27	28	29
30						

OCTOBER
S	M	T	W	T	F	S
	1	2	3	4	5	6
7	8	9	10	11	12	13
14	15	16	17	18	19	20
21	22	23	24	25	26	27
28	29	30	31			

NOVEMBER
S	M	T	W	T	F	S
				1	2	3
4	5	6	7	8	9	10
11	12	13	14	15	16	17
18	19	20	21	22	23	24
25	26	27	28	29	30	

DECEMBER
S	M	T	W	T	F	S
						1
2	3	4	5	6	7	8
9	10	11	12	13	14	15
16	17	18	19	20	21	22
23	24	25	26	27	28	29
30	31					